ILLINOIS
POST OFFICE
MURAL
GUIDEBOOK

DAVID W. GATES JR.

POST OFFICE FANS
Crystal Lake, Illinois

Post Office Fans
PO Box 11
Crystal Lake, IL 60039
Phone: 815-206-8405
info@postofficefans.com • www.postofficefans.com

Cover and text design by John Reinhardt Book Design
Front cover photo: Hamilton Post Office, Hamilton, Illinois

Contents

Illinois Post Office Murals

1 Abingdon
2 Berwyn
3 Brookfield
4 Bushnell
5 Carlyle
6 Carmi
7 Carthage
8 Chester
9 Chicago-Chestnut
   (former)
10 Chicago-Chestnut
   (former)
11 Chicago-Kedzie
12 Chicago-Lakeview
13 Chicago-Logan Square
14 Chicago-Morgan Park
15 Chicago-Uptown
16 Chillicothe
17 Clinton
18 Decatur
19 Des Plaines (former)
20 Downers Grove
21 Dwight
22 East Alton
23 East Moline
24 Eldorado
25 Elmhurst
26 Evanston
27 Fairfield
28 Flora
29 Forest Park
30 Galesburg
31 Geneva
32 Gibson City
33 Gillespie
34 Glen Ellyn
35 Hamilton
36 Herrin
37 Homewood

38 Kankakee
39 Lemont
40 Lewistown
41 Madison
42 Marseilles
43 Marshall
44 McLeansboro
45 Melrose Park
   (former)
46 Moline
47 Morton
48 Mount Carroll
49 Mount Morris
50 Mount Sterling
51 Naperville (former)
52 Nashville
53 Nokomis
54 Normal
55 Oak Park
56 O'Fallon
57 Oglesby
58 Oregon
59 Park Ridge (former)
60 Peoria (former)
61 Petersburg
62 Pittsfield
63 Plano
64 Rock Falls
65 Rushville
66 Salem (former)
67 Sandwich
68 Shelbyville
69 Staunton
70 Tuscola
71 Vandalia
72 Virden
73 White Hall
74 Wilmette
75 Wood River

PREFACE

THE STATISTICS I'VE READ report there are somewhere between 1,100 and 1,400 works of art located in public post offices nationwide. Since I've been unable to verify these statistics, I've made it my mission to find out exactly how many exist and to view them all.

What began for me as a casual interest in a photographic subject soon became a deep fascination with the history and presence of a unique moment in American culture and art. Before creating this guidebook, I visited hundreds of post offices and spoke to dozens of people across the U.S., and I realized we were united in our enthusiasm for keeping the stories of this art alive and available for the American public.

The guidebook you are viewing today is an account of all 75 of Illinois's New Deal post office murals. I encourage you to visit one of these post offices in Illinois or seek out one in your own state. To learn about this special art is to learn about the continuing American journey.

Our guidebooks continue to be a great resource for post office enthusiasts. Since I'm from Illinois, I found it fitting to create one for the Land of Lincoln. This led to the book you are holding today. It provides a quick reference to the Depression-era murals in Illinois.

There are no images of the murals in this book. It is meant solely as a reference to the buildings and towns. This guide provides: full address, title of the artwork, artist, medium, and status. I've found having a book like this makes for a handy reference and personal checklist while traveling around the state.

I've created this guidebook for your benefit, in case you find yourself needing the same checklist as you travel and discover each building and mural. I hope this book brings you enjoyment and knowledge. There is no need to scour multiple sources to find the status of each one. I've done the work for you. Print it out or download it to your mobile device to bring with you on your next post office visit.

Thank you,

David W. Gates Jr.

INTRODUCTION

FROM 1934–1943, fascinating murals and various forms of art were commissioned and installed in public buildings under the United States Treasury Department's Section of Painting and Sculpture, later renamed the Section of Fine Arts.

My research revealed two reasons for installing art in post offices. The first was to bring light and hope to a country gripped by the Great Depression, and the second was to employ artists during this difficult time.

Anonymous competitions were held to select artists for new federal buildings that were being constructed during this time. Commissions paid to the artists were approximately one percent of the congressional appropriation to construct the new post office buildings.

This informative book lists all the post offices in Illinois that received artwork. It gives you a quick reference to the New Deal post office murals in Illinois. It includes:

- Full address
- Artist
- Title
- Medium
- Status
- Link for further reading

While this guide does not provide images of the actual art, it does provide you a quick reference to the post office art in Illinois. Although the title of the book says "mural," I use that term inclusively. Illinois is lucky to have also receive art commissioned in other mediums such as wood, plaster, ceramic tile, terra-cotta, stone, and aluminum.

Abingdon

Address: 123 W. Meek St., Abingdon, Illinois 61410

Artist: Newell Hillis Arnold

Title: *Post Rider*

Medium: Terra-cotta (relief)

Status: The Abingdon post office is still an active, operating facility, and the relief can be viewed by interested members of the public. It resides in the lobby on the wall above the postmaster's door.

Web: https://www.postofficefans.com/abingdon-illinois-post-office/

BERWYN

ADDRESS: 6625 Cermak Rd., Berwyn, Illinois 60402

Artist: Richard Haines

TITLE: *The Picnic*

MEDIUM: Oil on canvas (mural)

STATUS: The Berwyn post office is still an active, operating facility, and the mural can be viewed by interested members of the public. It resides in the lobby on the wall above the postmaster's door.

WEB: https://www.postofficefans.com/berwyn-illinois-post-office/

BROOKFIELD

ADDRESS: 3731 Prairie Ave., Brookfield, Illinois 60513

ARTIST: Edouard Chassaing

TITLE: *Means of Mail Transportation*

MEDIUM: Plaster (relief)

STATUS: The Brookfield post office is still an active, operating facility, and the relief can be viewed by interested members of the public. It resides in the lobby on the wall above the postmaster's door.

WEB: https://www.postofficefans.com/brookfield-illinois-post-office/

BUSHNELL

ADDRESS: 223 E. Hail St., Bushnell, Illinois 61422

ARTIST: Reva Jackman

TITLE: *Pioneer Home in Bushnell*

MEDIUM: Oil on canvas (mural)

STATUS: The Bushnell post office is still an active, operating facility, and the mural can be viewed by interested members of the public. It resides in the lobby on the wall above the postmaster's door.

WEB: https://www.postofficefans.com/bushnell-illnois-post-office/

CARLYLE

ADDRESS: 1080 Fairfax St., Carlyle, Illinois 62231

ARTIST: Curt Drewes

TITLE: *Fish Hatchery, Farm*, and *Dairy Farming*

MEDIUM: Stone (reliefs)

STATUS: The Carlyle post office is still an active, operating facility, and the reliefs can be viewed by interested members of the public. They reside in the lobby on the wall above the postmaster's door.

WEB: https://www.postofficefans.com/carlyle-illinois-post-office/

CARMI

ADDRESS: 201 S. Walnut St., Carmi, Illinois 62821

ARTIST: William Davenport Griffen

TITLE: *Service to the Farmer*

MEDIUM: Oil on canvas (mural)

STATUS: The Carmi post office is still an active, operating facility, and the mural can be viewed by interested members of the public. It resides in the lobby on the wall above the postmaster's door.

WEB: https://www.postofficefans.com/carmi-illinois-post-office/

CARTHAGE

ADDRESS: 615 Main St., Carthage, Illinois 62321

ARTIST: Karl Kelpe

TITLE: *Pioneers—Tilling the Soil and Building Log Cabin*

MEDIUM: Oil on canvas (mural)

STATUS: The Carthage post office is still an active, operating facility, and the mural can be viewed by interested members of the public. It resides in the lobby on the wall above the postmaster's door.

WEB: https://www.postofficefans.com/carthage-illinois-post-office/

ADDRESS: 1321 Swanwick St., Chester, Illinois 62233

ARTIST: Fay Elizabeth Davis

TITLE: *Loading the Packet*

MEDIUM: Tempera (mural)

STATUS: The Chester post office is still an active, operating facility, and the mural can be viewed by interested members of the public. It resides in the lobby on the wall above the postmaster's door.

WEB: https://www.postofficefans.com/chester-illinois-post-office/

CHICAGO

FORMER CHESTNUT/CARDISS COLLINS

ADDRESS: 433 W. Harrison St., Chicago, Illinois 60699

ARTIST: Frances Foy

TITLE: *Advent of the Pioneer, 1851*

MEDIUM: Oil on canvas (mural)

STATUS: The mural on display here was originally one of two murals installed in the Chicago–Chestnut Station post office. The historic Chestnut Station building was razed in 2003. The mural was relocated here, to the Chicago–Cardiss Collins facility. It resides on a wall in the 1st floor lobby.

Web: https://www.postofficefans.com/chicago-illinois-cardiss-collins-post-office/

ADDRESS: 211 S. Clark St., Chicago, Illinois 60604

ARTIST: Gustaf Dalstrom

TITLE: *Great Indian Council, Chicago, 1833*

MEDIUM: Oil on canvas (mural)

STATUS: The mural on display here was originally one of two murals installed in the Chicago–Chestnut Station post office. The historic Chestnut Station building was razed in 2003. The mural was relocated here, to the Loop Clark Street facility. The mural resides on the wall in the lobby.

WEB: https://www.postofficefans.com/chicago-illinois-loop-post-office/

CHICAGO–
KEDZIE

ADDRESS: 3750 N. Kedzie Ave., Chicago, Illinois 60618

ARTIST: Peterpaul Ott

TITLE: *Mercury*

MEDIUM: Aluminum (relief)

STATUS: The Chicago–Kedzie post office is still an active, operating facility. It is also known as the Daniel J. Doffyn Station. The relief can be viewed by interested members of the public. It resides on the wall in the retail section of the lobby and is viewable during business hours.

WEB: https://www.postofficefans.com/chicago-illinois-daniel-j-doffyn-post-office/

CHICAGO– LAKEVIEW

ADDRESS: 1343 W. Irving Park Rd., Chicago, Illinois 60613

ARTIST: Harry Sternberg

TITLE: *Chicago: Epoch of a Great City*

MEDIUM: Oil on canvas (mural)

STATUS: The Chicago–Lakeview post office is still an active, operating facility, and the mural can be viewed by interested members of the public. It resides in the lobby on the wall above the retail counter.

WEB: https://www.postofficefans.com/chicago-illinois-lakeview-post-office/

CHICAGO–
LOGAN SQUARE

ADDRESS: 2339 N. California, Ave., Chicago, Illinois 60647

ARTIST: Hildreth Meière

TITLE: *The Post*

MEDIUM: Metal (design)

STATUS: The Chicago–Logan Square post office is still an active, operating facility. It is also known a the Roberto Clemente Station. The metal design can be viewed by interested members of the public. It resides in the lobby on the wall above the retail entrance.

Web: https://www.postofficefans.com/chicago-illinois-logan-square-post-office/

CHICAGO–
MORGAN PARK

ADDRESS: 1805 W. Monterey Ave., Chicago, Illinois 60643

ARTIST: John Theodore Johnson

TITLE: *Father Marquette—1674*

MEDIUM: Oil on canvas (mural)

STATUS: The Chicago–Morgan Park post office is still an active, operating facility, and the mural can be viewed by interested members of the public. It resides in the lobby on the wall above the
bulletin boards.

WEB: https://www.postofficefans.com/chicago-illinois-morgan-
park-station-post-office/

CHICAGO–
UPTOWN

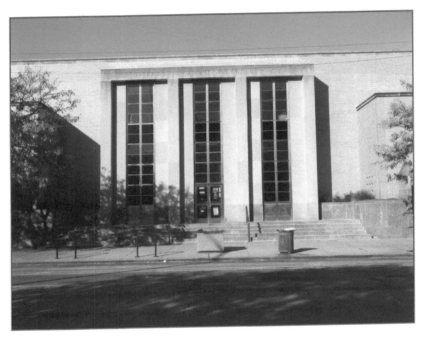

ADDRESS: 4850 N. Broadway St., Chicago, Illinois 60640

ARTIST: Henry Varnum Poor

TITLE: *Carl Sandburg* and *Louis Sullivan*

MEDIUM: Ceramic (tiles)

STATUS: The Chicago–Uptown post office is still an active, operating facility, and the tiles can be viewed by interested members of the public. The tiles are located in the lobby on the wall above the retail counter.

WEB: https://www.postofficefans.com/chicago-illinois-uptown-station-post-office/

CHILLICOTHE

ADDRESS: 1114 N. 2nd St., Chillicothe, Illinois 61523

ARTIST: Arthur Herschel Lidov

TITLE: *Rail Roading*

MEDIUM: Egg tempera (mural)

STATUS: The Chillicothe post office is still an active, operating facility, and the mural can be viewed by interested members of the public. It resides in the lobby on the wall above the postmaster's door.

WEB: https://www.postofficefans.com/chillicothe-illinois-post-office/

CLINTON

ADDRESS: 105 N. Quincy St., Clinton, Illinois 61727

ARTIST: Aaron Bohrod

TITLE: *Clinton in Winter*

MEDIUM: Oil on canvas (mural)

STATUS: The Clinton post office is still an active, operating facility, and the mural can be viewed by interested members of the public. It resides in the lobby on the wall above the postmaster's door.

WEB: https://www.postofficefans.com/clinton-illinois-post-office/

DECATUR

ADDRESS: 214 N. Franklin St., Decatur, Illinois 62523

ARTIST: Edward Millman

TITLE: *Early Pioneers, Social Consciousness,* and *Growth of Democracy in Illinois*

MEDIUM: Fresco (murals)

STATUS: The Decatur post office is still an active, operating facility, and the murals can be viewed by interested members of the public. They reside on the walls throughout the main lobby.

WEB: https://www.postofficefans.com/decatur-illinois-post-office/

DECATUR
(CONT'D)

ADDRESS: 214 N. Franklin St., Decatur, Illinois 62523

ARTIST: Edgar Britton

TITLE: *Natural Resources of Illinois—Frank Lloyd Wright and Carl Sandburg, Natural Resources of Illinois—John Deere and Francis Parker*, and *Development of Illinois*

MEDIUM: Fresco (murals)

STATUS: The Decatur post office is still an active, operating facility, and the murals can be viewed by interested members of the public. They reside on the walls throughout the main lobby.

WEB: https://www.postofficefans.com/decatur-illinois-post-office/

ADDRESS: 214 N. Franklin St., Decatur, Illinois 62523

ARTIST: Mitchell Siporin

TITLE: *The Fusion of Agriculture and Industry*

MEDIUM: Fresco (murals), 3 murals

STATUS: The Decatur post office is still an active, operating facility, and the murals can be viewed by interested members of the public. They reside on the walls throughout the main lobby.

WEB: https://www.postofficefans.com/decatur-illinois-post-office/

Des Plaines

ADDRESS: 622 Graceland Ave., Des Plaines, Illinois 60016

ARTIST: James Michael Newell

TITLE: *Father Marquette* and *Conquest of the Prairie Lands*

MEDIUM: Fresco (murals)

STATUS: The former Des Plaines post office is now privately owned by Journal & Topics. Interested members of the public should contact Journal & Topics before visiting to see the murals. As of this publication, they reside on the walls of what was once the original lobby.

WEB: https://www.postofficefans.com/former-des-plaines-illinois-post-office/

DOWNERS GROVE

ADDRESS: 920 Curtiss St., Downers Grove, Illinois 60515

ARTIST: Elizabeth Tracy

TITLE: *Chicago, Railroad Center of the Nation*

MEDIUM: Oil on canvas (mural)

STATUS: The Downers Grove post office is still an active, operating facility, and the mural can be viewed by interested members of the public. It resides in the lobby on the wall above the postmaster's door.

WEB: https://www.postofficefans.com/downers-grove-illinois-post-office/

DWIGHT

ADDRESS: 100 E. Mazon Ave., Dwight, Illinois 60420

ARTIST: Carlos Lopez

TITLE: *The Stage at Dawn*

MEDIUM: Fresco (mural)

STATUS: The Dwight post office is still an active, operating facility, and the mural can be viewed by interested members of the public. It resides in the lobby on the wall above the postmaster's door.

WEB: https://www.postofficefans.com/dwight-illinois-post-office/

ADDRESS: 200 Smith Ave., East Alton, Illinois 62024

ARTIST: Frances Foy

TITLE: *The Letter*

MEDIUM: Oil on canvas (mural)

STATUS: The East Alton post office is still an active, operating facility, and the mural can be viewed by interested members of the public. It resides in the retail section of the lobby on the wall above the postmaster's door.

WEB: https://www.postofficefans.com/east-alton-illinois-post-office/

East Moline

Address: 805 16th Ave., East Moline, Illinois 61244

Artist: Edgar Britton

Title: *Early Settlers of Moline along the Mississippi*

Medium: Fresco (mural)

Status: The East Moline post office is still an active, operating facility, and the mural can be viewed by interested members of the public. It resides in the lobby on the wall next to the staircase.

Web: https://www.postofficefans.com/east-moline-illinois-post-office/

ELDORADO

ADDRESS: 900 4th St., Eldorado, Illinois 62930

ARTIST: William Samuel Schwartz

TITLE: *Mining in Illinois*

MEDIUM: Oil on canvas (mural)

STATUS: The Eldorado post office is still an active, operating facility, and the mural can be viewed by interested members of the public. It resides in the lobby on the wall above the postmaster's door.

WEB: https://www.postofficefans.com/eldorado-illinois-post-office/

Elmhurst

ADDRESS: 154 W. Park Ave., Elmhurst, Illinois 60126

ARTIST: George Melville Smith

TITLE: *There Was Vision*

MEDIUM: Oil on canvas (mural)

STATUS: The Elmhurst post office is still an active, operating facility, and the mural can be viewed by interested members of the public. It resides in the lobby on the wall above the postmaster's door.

WEB: https://www.postofficefans.com/elmhurst-illinois-post-office/

ADDRESS: 1101 Davis St., Evanston, Illinois 60201

ARTIST: Robert Isaiah Russin

TITLE: *Throwing the Mail* and *Mail Handler*

MEDIUM: Cast aluminum with gold leaf (reliefs)

STATUS: The Evanston post office is still an active, operating facility, and the reliefs can be viewed by interested members of the public. They reside on the wall of the main lobby.

WEB: https://www.postofficefans.com/evanston-illinois-post-office/

EVANSTON

(CONT'D)

ADDRESS: 1101 Davis St., Evanston, Illinois 60201

ARTIST: Armin Alfred Scheler

TITLE: *The Message* and *The Answer*

MEDIUM: Limestone (reliefs)

STATUS: The Evanston post office is still an active, operating facility, and the reliefs can be viewed by interested members of the public. They reside on the exterior of the building above the entrance doors.

WEB: https://www.postofficefans.com/evanston-illinois-post-office/

FAIRFIELD

ADDRESS: 220 E. Delaware St., Fairfield, Illinois 62837

ARTIST: William Samuel Schwartz

TITLE: *Old Settlers*

MEDIUM: Oil on canvas (mural)

STATUS: The Fairfield post office is still an active, operating facility, and the mural can be viewed by interested members of the public. It resides in the lobby on the wall above the postmaster's door.

WEB: https://www.postofficefans.com/fairfield-illinois-post-office/

FLORA

ADDRESS: 312 E. North Ave., Flora, Illinois 62839

ARTIST: William Davenport Griffen

TITLE: *Good News and Bad*

MEDIUM: Oil on canvas (mural)

STATUS: The Flora post office is still an active, operating facility, and the mural can be viewed by interested members of the public. It resides in the lobby on the wall above the postmaster's door.

WEB: https://www.postofficefans.com/flora-illinois-post-office/

FOREST PARK

ADDRESS: 417 Des Plaines Ave., Forest Park, Illinois 60130

ARTIST: Miriam McKinnie Hofmeier

TITLE: *The White Fawn*

MEDIUM: Oil on canvas (mural)

STATUS: The Forest Park post office is still an active, operating facility, and the mural can be viewed by interested members of the public. It resides in the lobby on the wall above the postmaster's door.

WEB: https://www.postofficefans.com/forest-park-illinois-post-office/

GALESBURG

ADDRESS: 476 E. Main St., Galesburg, Illinois 61401

ARTIST: Aaron Bohrod

TITLE: *Breaking the Prairie—Log City, 1837*

MEDIUM: Oil on canvas (mural)

STATUS: The Galesburg post office is still an active, operating facility, and the mural can be viewed by interested members of the public. It resides on a wall in the main lobby.

WEB: https://www.postofficefans.com/galesburg-illinois-post-office/

GENEVA

ADDRESS: 26 S. 3rd St., Geneva, Illinois 60134

ARTIST: Manuel Abraham Bromberg

TITLE: *Fish Fry in the Park*

MEDIUM: Tempera (mural)

STATUS: The Geneva post office is still an active, operating facility, and the mural can be viewed by interested members of the public. It resides in the lobby on the wall above the postmaster's door.

WEB: https://www.postofficefans.com/geneva-illinois-post-office/

GIBSON CITY

ADDRESS: 127 E. 9th St., Gibson City, Illinois 60936

ARTIST: Frances Foy

TITLE: *Hiawatha Returning with Minnehaha*

MEDIUM: Oil on canvas (mural)

STATUS: The Gibson City post office is still an active, operating facility, and the mural can be viewed by interested members of the public. It resides in the lobby on the wall above the postmaster's door.

WEB: https://www.postofficefans.com/gibson-city-illinois-post-office/

GILLESPIE

ADDRESS: 200 W. Spruce St., Gillespie, Illinois 62033

ARTIST: Gustaf Dalstrom

TITLE: *Illinois Farm*

MEDIUM: Oil on canvas (mural)

STATUS: The Gillespie post office is still an active, operating facility, and the mural can be viewed by interested members of the public. It resides in the lobby on the wall above the postmaster's door.

WEB: https://www.postofficefans.com/gillespie-illinois-post-office/

GLEN ELLYN

ADDRESS: 528 Pennsylvania Ave., Glen Ellyn, Illinois 60137

ARTIST: Daniel Rhodes

TITLE: *Settlers Building*

MEDIUM: Oil on canvas (mural)

STATUS: The Glen Ellyn post office is still an active, operating facility, and the mural can be viewed by interested members of the public. It resides in the lobby on the wall above the postmaster's door.

WEB: https://www.postofficefans.com/Glen-ellyn-illinois-down-town-post-office/

HAMILTON

ADDRESS: 1160 Broadway St., Hamilton, Illinois 62341

ARTIST: Edmund D. Lewandowski

TITLE: *On The River*

MEDIUM: Oil on canvas (mural)

STATUS: The Hamilton post office is still an active, operating facility, and the mural can be viewed by interested members of the public. It resides in the lobby on the wall above the postmaster's door.

WEB: https://www.postofficefans.com/hamilton-illinois-post-office/

HERRIN

ADDRESS: 200 S. Park Ave., Herrin, Illinois 62948

ARTIST: Gustaf Dalstrom

TITLE: *George Rogers Clark Conferring with Indians near Herrin, Illinois*

MEDIUM: Oil on canvas (mural)

STATUS: The Herrin post office is still an active, operating facility, and the mural can be viewed by interested members of the public. For years, the mural was reported to have been lost or destroyed. However, it has been recovered and wonderfully restored. It resides on a wall in the retail section of the lobby.

WEB: https://www.postofficefans.com/herrin-illinois-post-office/

HOMEWOOD

ADDRESS: 1921 Ridge Rd., Homewood, Illinois 60430

ARTIST: Maurine Montgomery Gibbs

TITLE: *The Letter*

MEDIUM: Wood (relief)

STATUS: The Homewood post office is still an active, operating facility, and the relief can be viewed by interested members of the public. It resides in the lobby on the wall above the postmaster's door.

WEB: https://www.postofficefans.com/homewood-illinois-post-office/

KANKAKEE

ADDRESS: 475 E. Court St., Kankakee, Illinois 60901

ARTIST: Edouard Chassaing

TITLE: *Farming*

MEDIUM: Wood (carvings)

STATUS: The Kankakee post office is still an active, operating facility, and the carvings can be viewed by interested members of the public. They reside in the lobby on the wall above the postmaster's door.

WEB: https://www.postofficefans.com/kankakee-illinois-post-office/

LEMONT

ADDRESS: 42 Stephen St., Lemont, Illinois 60439

ARTIST: Charles Turzak

TITLE: *Canal Boats*

MEDIUM: Oil on canvas (mural)

STATUS: The Lemont post office is still an active, operating facility, and the mural can be viewed by interested members of the public. It resides in the lobby on the wall above the postmaster's door.

WEB: https://www.postofficefans.com/lemont-illinois-post-office/

LEWISTOWN

ADDRESS: 301 N. Main St., Lewistown, Illinois 61542

ARTIST: Ida Abelman

TITLE: *Lewistown Milestones*

MEDIUM: Tempera (mural)

STATUS: The Lewistown post office is still an active, operating facility, and the mural can be viewed by interested members of the public. It resides in the lobby on the wall above the postmaster's door.

WEB: https://www.postofficefans.com/lewistown-illinois-post-office/

MADISON

ADDRESS: 549 Madison Ave., Madison, Illinois 62060

ARTIST: Alexander Raymond Katz

TITLE: *Assimilation of the Immigrant into the Industrial Life of Madison*

MEDIUM: Oil on canvas (mural)

STATUS: The Madison post office is still an active, operating facility, and the mural can be viewed by interested members of the public. It resides in the lobby on the wall above the postmaster's door.

WEB: https://www.postofficefans.com/madison-illinois-post-office/

MARSEILLES

ADDRESS: 100 Washington St., Marseilles, Illinois 61341

ARTIST: Avery Johnson

TITLE: *Industrial Marseilles*

MEDIUM: Oil on canvas (mural)

STATUS: The Marseilles post office is still an active, operating facility, and the mural can be viewed by interested members of the public. It resides in the lobby on the wall above the postmaster's door.

WEB: https://www.postofficefans.com/marseilles-illinois-post-office/

MARSHALL

ADDRESS: 115 N. 7th St., Marshall, Illinois 62441

ARTIST: Miriam McKinnie Hofmeier

TITLE: *Harvest*

MEDIUM: Oil on canvas (mural)

STATUS: The Marshall post office is still an active, operating facility, and the mural can be viewed by interested members of the public. It resides in the lobby on the wall above the postmaster's door.

WEB: https://www.postofficefans.com/marshall-illinois-post-office/

McLeansboro

ADDRESS: 211 S. Jackson St., McLeansboro, Illinois 62859

ARTIST: Dorothea Mierisch

TITLE: *First Official Air Mail Flight*

MEDIUM: Oil on canvas (mural)

STATUS: The McLeansboro post office is still an active, operating facility, and the mural can be viewed by interested members of the public. It resides in the lobby on the wall above the postmaster's door.

WEB: https://www.postofficefans.com/mcleansboro-illinois-post-office/

MELROSE PARK

ADDRESS: 801 N. 19 Ave., Melrose Park, Illinois 60160

ARTIST: Edwin Boyd Johnson

TITLE: *Air Mail*

MEDIUM: Fresco (mural)

STATUS: The Melrose Park post office closed in the 1960s. The mural was hidden by a drop ceiling and forgotten about for years. The public library purchased and remodeled the building considerably. The mural was restored and it resides in the adult services section for all to enjoy.

WEB: https://www.postofficefans.com/former-melrose-park-illinois-post-office/

Moline

Address: 514 17th St., Moline, Illinois 61265

Artist: Edward Millman

Title: *Ploughshare Manufacturing*

Medium: Egg tempera (mural)

Status: The Moline post office is still an active, operating facility, and the mural can be viewed by interested members of the public. It resides in the main lobby on the wall above the entrance.

Web: https://www.postofficefans.com/moline-illinois-post-office/

MORTON

ADDRESS: 120 N. Main St., Morton, Illinois 61550

ARTIST: Charles Umlauf

TITLE: *Spirit of Communication*

MEDIUM: Stone (relief)

STATUS: The relief no longer resides in the original building shown here. It was moved to the newer post office building on Jefferson St. It resides in the retail section of the lobby and is best viewed during business hours.

WEB: https://www.postofficefans.com/former-morton-illinois-post-office/

MOUNT CARROLL

ADDRESS: 211 N. Clay St., Mount Carroll, Illinois 61053

ARTIST: Irene Soravia Bianucci

TITLE: *Rural Scenes—Wakarusa Valley*

MEDIUM: Oil on canvas (mural)

STATUS: The Mount Carroll post office is still an active, operating facility, and the mural can be viewed by interested members of the public. It resides in the lobby on the wall above the postmaster's door.

WEB: https://www.postofficefans.com/mount-carroll-illinois-post-office/

MOUNT MORRIS

ADDRESS: 21 W. Main St., Mount Morris, Illinois 61054

ARTIST: Dale Nichols

TITLE: *The Growth of Mount Morris*

MEDIUM: Oil on canvas (mural)

STATUS: The Mount Morris post office is still an active, operating facility, and the mural can be viewed by interested members of the public. It resides in the lobby on the wall above the postmaster's door.

WEB: https://www.postofficefans.com/mount-morris-illlinois-post-office/

MOUNT STERLING

ADDRESS: 130 W. Main St., Mount Sterling, Illinois 62353

ARTIST: Henry Bernstein

TITLE: *The Covered Bridge*

MEDIUM: Tempera (mural)

STATUS: The Mount Sterling post office is still an active, operating facility, and the mural can be viewed by interested members of the public. It resides in the lobby on the wall above the postmaster's door.

WEB: https://www.postofficefans.com/mount-sterling-illinois-post-office/

NAPERVILLE

ADDRESS: 5 S. Washington St., Naperville, Illinois 60540

ARTIST: Rainey Bennett

TITLE: *George Martin's Home Overlooking Old Naper Hill*

MEDIUM: Oil on canvas (mural)

STATUS: The former Naperville post office is now Naperville Bank & Trust. The mural can be viewed by interested members of the public during business hours. It resides on the wall behind the teller's counter.

WEB: https://www.postofficefans.com/former-and-new-naperville-illinois-post-office/

NASHVILLE

ADDRESS: 181 S. Kaskaskia St., Nashville, Illinois 62263

ARTIST: Zoltan Sepeshy

TITLE: *Barnyard*

MEDIUM: Tempera (mural)

STATUS: The Nashville post office is still an active, operating facility, and the mural can be viewed by interested members of the public. It resides in the lobby on the wall above the post office boxes.

WEB: https://www.postofficefans.com/nashville-illinois-post-office/

NOKOMIS

ADDRESS: 121 S. Pine St., Nokomis, Illinois 62075

ARTIST: Bernard J. Rosenthal

TITLE: *Coal Mining*

MEDIUM: Wood (carving)

STATUS: The Nokomis post office is still an active, operating facility, and the carving can be viewed by interested members of the public. It resides in the lobby on the wall above the postmaster's door.

WEB: https://www.postofficefans.com/nokomis-illinois-post-office/

NORMAL

ADDRESS: 200 W. North St., Normal, Illinois 61761

ARTIST: Albert Pels

TITLE: *Development of the State Normal School*

MEDIUM: Oil on canvas (mural)

STATUS: The Normal post office is still an active, operating facility, and the mural can be viewed by interested members of the public. It resides in the lobby on the wall above the postmaster's door.

WEB: https://www.postofficefans.com/normal-illinois-post-office/

OAK PARK

ADDRESS: 901 Lake St., Oak Park, Illinois 60301

ARTIST: John Theodore Johnson

TITLE: *History of Chicago*

MEDIUM: Oil on canvas (murals), 4 panels

STATUS: The Oak Park post office is still an active, operating facility, and the murals can be viewed by interested members of the public. They reside on the walls in the main lobby.

WEB: https://www.postofficefans.com/oak-park-illinois-post-office-part-2-mural-1/

O'FALLON

ADDRESS: 1111 S. Lincoln Ave., O'Fallon, Illinois 62269

ARTIST: Merlin F. Pollock

TITLE: *John Mason Peck, First Postmaster Handing Out Mail—1830*

MEDIUM: Oil on canvas (mural)

STATUS: The former historic O'Fallon post office building was razed. However, the mural can be viewed by interested members of the public in the newer building pictured here. It resides on the wall above the retail counter.

WEB: https://www.postofficefans.com/o-fallon-illinois-post-office/

OGLESBY

ADDRESS: 203 W. Walnut St., Oglesby, Illinois 61348

ARTIST: Fay Elizabeth Davis

TITLE: *The Illini and Potawatomi Struggle at Starved Rock*

MEDIUM: Oil on canvas (mural)

STATUS: The Oglesby post office is still an active, operating facility, and the mural can be viewed by interested members of the public. It resides in the lobby on the wall above the postmaster's door.

WEB: https://www.postofficefans.com/oglesby-illinois-post-office/

OREGON

ADDRESS: 500 W. Washington, St., Oregon, Illinois 61061

ARTIST: David B. Cheskin

TITLE: *The Pioneer and Democracy*

MEDIUM: Tempera (mural)

STATUS: The Oregon post office is still an active, operating facility, and the mural can be viewed by interested members of the public. It resides in the lobby on the wall above the postmaster's door.

WEB: https://www.postofficefans.com/oregon-illinois-post-office/

PARK RIDGE

ADDRESS: 164 S. Prospect Ave., Park Ridge, Illinois 60068

ARTIST: George Melville Smith

TITLE: *Indians Cede the Land*

MEDIUM: Oil on canvas (mural)

STATUS: The former Park Ridge post office is now owned by the local school district. The mural was restored and relocated to the Park Ridge public library where it can be viewed by interested members of the public.

WEB: https://www.postofficefans.com/former-park-ridge-illinois-post-office/

PEORIA

Address: 100 NE Monroe St., Peoria, Illinois 61602

Artist: Freeman Schoolcraft

Title: *Postal Service*, *Native Indian*, *Agriculture*, and *Industry*

Medium: Limestone (reliefs)

Status: The Peoria courthouse is still an active, operating facility. However, the post office no longer operates out of this building. The reliefs can be viewed by interested members of the public. They reside on the exterior of the building.

Web: https://www.postofficefans.com/former-peoria-illinois-post-office-courthouse/

PETERSBURG

ADDRESS: 220 S. 7th St., Petersburg, Illinois 62675

ARTIST: John Winters

TITLE: *Lincoln at New Salem, Illinois*

MEDIUM: Oil on canvas (mural)

STATUS: The Petersburg post office is still an active, operating facility, and the mural can be viewed by interested members of the public. It resides in the lobby on the wall above the postmaster's door.

WEB: https://www.postofficefans.com/petersburg-illinois-post-office/

PITTSFIELD

ADDRESS: 129 S. Madison St., Pittsfield, Illinois 62363

ARTIST: William Samuel Schwartz

TITLE: *River Boat and Bridge*

MEDIUM: Oil on canvas (mural)

STATUS: The Pittsfield post office is still an active, operating facility, and the mural can be viewed by interested members of the public. It resides in the lobby on the wall above the postmaster's door.

WEB: https://www.postofficefans.com/pittsfield-illinois-post-office/

PLANO

ADDRESS: 102 N. Center St., Plano, Illinois 60545

ARTIST: Perterpaul Ott

TITLE: *Harvest*

MEDIUM: Wood (carvings)

STATUS: The Plano post office is still an active, operating facility, and the wood carvings can be viewed by interested members of the public. They reside in the lobby on the wall above the bulletin boards.

WEB: https://www.postofficefans.com/plano-illinois-post-office/

ROCK FALLS

ADDRESS: 210 2nd Ave., Rock Falls, Illinois 61071

ARTIST: Curt Drewes

TITLE: *Farming by Hand* and *The Manufacture of Farm Implements*

MEDIUM: Plaster (reliefs)

STATUS: The Rock Falls post office is still an active, operating facility, and the reliefs can be viewed by interested members of the public. They reside in the lobby on the wall above the post-master's door.

WEB: https://www.postofficefans.com/rock-falls-illinois-post-office/

ADDRESS: 101 E. Washington St., Rushville, Illinois 62681

ARTIST: Rainey Bennett

TITLE: *Hart Fellows—Builder of Rushville*

MEDIUM: Oil on canvas (mural)

STATUS: The Rushville post office is still an active, operating facility, and the mural can be viewed by interested members of the public. It resides in the lobby on the wall above the postmaster's door.

WEB: https://www.postofficefans.com/rushville-illinois-post-office/

Salem

ADDRESS: 217 W. Main St., Salem, Illinois 62881

ARTIST: Walter Vladimir Rousseff

TITLE: *Lincoln as Postmaster in New Salem*

MEDIUM: Oil on canvas (mural)

STATUS: The former Salem post office was occupied by a local business. As of the date of this publication, it appears to be vacant. The mural was relocated to the local library, and can be viewed by interested members of the public. It resides in a conference room.

WEB: https://www.postofficefans.com/former-salem-illinois-post-office/

SANDWICH

ADDRESS: 22 N. Eddy St., Sandwich, Illinois 60548

ARTIST: Marshall Maynard Fredericks

TITLE: *The Family*

MEDIUM: Terra-cotta (relief)

STATUS: The Sandwich post office is still an active, operating facility, and the relief can be viewed by interested members of the public. It resides in the lobby on the wall above the postmaster's door.

WEB: https://www.postofficefans.com/sandwich-illinois-post-office/

SHELBYVILLE

ADDRESS: 200 S. Morgan St., Shelbyville, Illinois 62565

ARTIST: Lucia May Wiley

TITLE: *Shelby County Fair—1900*

MEDIUM: Fresco (mural)

STATUS: The Shelbyville post office is still an active, operating facility, and the mural can be viewed by interested members of the public. It resides in the lobby on the wall above the postmaster's door.

WEB: https://www.postofficefans.com/shelbyville-illinois-post-office/

STAUNTON

ADDRESS: 113 S. Edwardsville St., Staunton, Illinois 62088

ARTIST: Ralf Christian Henricksen

TITLE: *Going to Work*

MEDIUM: Oil on canvas (mural)

STATUS: The Staunton post office is still an active, operating facility, and the mural can be viewed by interested members of the public. It resides in the lobby on the wall above the postmaster's door.

WEB: https://www.postofficefans.com/staunton-illinois-post-office/

Tuscola

ADDRESS: 120 E. Sale St., Tuscola, Illinois 61953

ARTIST: Edwin Boyd Johnson

TITLE: *The Old Days*

MEDIUM: Oil on canvas (mural)

STATUS: The Tuscola post office is still an active, operating facility, and the mural can be viewed by interested members of the public. It resides in the lobby on the wall above the postmaster's door.

WEB: https://www.postofficefans.com/tuscola-illinois-post-office/

VANDALIA

ADDRESS: 304 S. 4th St., Vandalia, Illinois 62471

ARTIST: Aaron Bohrod

TITLE: *Old State Capitol in Vandalia*

MEDIUM: Oil on canvas (mural)

STATUS: The Vandalia post office is still an active, operating facility, and the mural can be viewed by interested members of the public. It resides in the lobby on the wall above the postmaster's door.

WEB: https://www.postofficefans.com/vandalia-illinois-post-office/

VIRDEN

ADDRESS: 211 N. Springfield St., Virden, Illinois 62690

ARTIST: James Daugherty

TITLE: *Illinois Pastoral*

MEDIUM: Tempera and oil (mural)

STATUS: The Virden post office is still an active, operating facility, and the mural can be viewed by interested members of the public. It resides in the lobby on the wall above the postmaster's door.

WEB: https://www.postofficefans.com/virden-illinois-post-office/

WHITE HALL

ADDRESS: 120 S. Jacksonville St., White Hall, Illinois 62092

ARTIST: Felix Oscar Schlag

TITLE: *Potter and His Burro*

MEDIUM: Plaster (relief)

STATUS: The White Hall post office is still an active, operating facility, and the relief can be viewed by interested members of the public. It resides in the lobby on the wall above the postmaster's door.

WEB: https://www.postofficefans.com/white-hall-illinois-post-office/

WILMETTE

ADDRESS: 1241 Central Ave., Wilmette, Illinois 60091

ARTIST: Raymond Breinin

TITLE: *In the Soil Is Our Wealth*

MEDIUM: Oil on canvas (mural)

STATUS: The Wilmette post office is still an active, operating facility, and
the mural can be viewed by interested members of the public.
It resides in an office on the left side of the lobby. It's viewable
through the glass but difficult to see entirely unobstructed, un-
less you are in the office.

WEB: https://www.postofficefans.com/wilmette-illinois-post-office/

WOOD RIVER–ROXANA

ADDRESS: 161 E. Ferguson Ave., Wood River–Roxana, Illinois 62095

ARTIST: Archibald Motley Jr.

TITLE: *Stagecoach and Mail*

MEDIUM: Oil on canvas (mural)

STATUS: The Wood River–Roxana post office is still an active, operating facility, and the mural can be viewed by interested members of the public. It resides in the lobby on the wall above the postmaster's door.

WEB: https://www.postofficefans.com/wood-river-roxana-illinois-post-office/

Summary

I CREATED THIS BOOK as a reference for myself, as well as for those who are interested in these wonderful buildings and works of art. My goal is to provide you a valuable reference list of the buildings in Illinois that house murals. For more information about each one and to participate in the discussion of any of the buildings or art, please visit www.postofficefans.com.

This book contains all the post offices in Illinois that had art installed as a part of the New Deal. This book provides notes on the location, status, and accessibility of the art. I've personally visited and photographed each building and mural. Please note this is not a complete list of all the post office buildings constructed in Illinois during the New Deal, only the ones that housed art.

I welcome your comments, suggestions, or feedback. You may reach me through the following social channels. Of course, I also welcome mail through the United States Postal Service, C/O Post Office Fans, PO Box 11, Crystal Lake, IL 60039.

About the Author

DAVID W. GATES JR. is a post office enthusiast and award-winning author who has traveled thousands of miles nationwide in search of historic post office buildings and art. He blogs about his work at:

www.postofficefans.com

Although the murals have been around for more than 86 years, David discovered how often these are overlooked. Join David in his quest to visit them all.

He lives in Crystal Lake, IL with his wife and son. When not photographing and documenting post offices, he can be found cooking, baking, hiking, or involved in do-it-yourself projects at home, not necessarily all at once and not necessarily in that order.

OTHER TITLES BY THE PUBLISHER

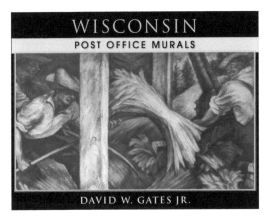

WISCONSIN POST OFFICE MURALS

by David W. Gates Jr.

ISBN: 978-1-970088-00-7 (Paperback)
ISBN: 978-1-970088-01-4 (EPUB)
ISBN: 978-1-970088-02-1 (PDF)

WISCONSIN POST OFFICE MURAL GUIDEBOOK

by David W. Gates Jr.

ISBN: 978-1-970088-09-0 (Paperback)
ISBN: 978-1-970088-10-6 (EPUB)
ISBN: 978-1-970088-11-3 (PDF)

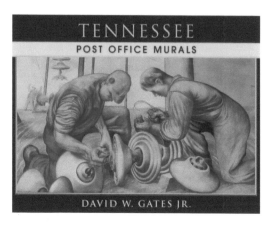

TENNESSEE POST OFFICE MURALS

by David W. Gates Jr.

ISBN: 978-1-970088-03-8 (Paperback)
ISBN: 978-1-970088-04-5 (EPUB)
ISBN: 978-1-970088-05-2 (PDF)

TENNESSEE POST OFFICE MURAL GUIDEBOOK

by David W. Gates Jr.

ISBN: 978-1-970088-06-9 (Paperback)
ISBN: 978-1-970088-07-6 (EPUB)
ISBN: 978-1-970088-08-3 (PDF)

Printed in the USA
CPSIA information can be obtained
at www.ICGtesting.com
LVHW071505300923
759797LV00006B/165

* 9 7 8 1 9 7 0 0 8 8 1 2 0 *